# INTRODUCTION

'Leg-over' is a strange expression. Nobody knows when or where it came from, or whose leg it is supposed to be over. His leg? Her leg? And at which address?

It could possibly have originated in the Australian outback, coined by remote farmers helping one another drunkenly into the sheep pens.

Or perhaps it refers to one of the more esoteric erotic positions only the great masters of eastern yoga can achieve.

Anyway, 'getting your leg over' is now understood by everyone over six to mean 'doing it' with person or persons of a like frame of mind, even if they don't understand what esoteric means.

The book arrived at the publishers in this scruffy ring-binder, and it is in this form that it now appears in print.

And please if there's anything you don't understand, don't be afraid to stick your hand up.

Fine. Now can we get on with it?

# CHAPTER 1: MEN THE BEAST IN YOU

Getting your leg over is a game. It is fun. It is what we are all programmed to do. It is not supposed to be a problem.

All men are born with a willie, a fact which some people regard as an enormous handicap, as if without this permanent distraction they would be nicer people, better able to concentrate upon the important things in life such as their wives.

Speaking as a willie, I must stress that the leg-over factor is not a ball and chain, but a wonderful bonus that can give years of pleasure and the odd slap in the face. Admittedly, having a willie makes it almost impossible to give anything your undivided attention, but what is so important that you can't dally and daydream every ten minutes?

Some men have no self-restraint and don't know how to behave themselves. Of course, they never get lucky and deserve everything they don't get. They also get the rest of us a bad name, like 'BASTARD'!

# WILLIE'S LEG-OVER HANDBOOK

Written and
illustrated by
GRAY JOLLIFFE

Pan Books
London, Sydney and
Auckland

First published 1991 by
Pan Books Ltd
Cavaye Place,
London SW10 9PG
9 8 7 6 5 4 3 2 1
© Gray Jolliffe 1991
ISBN 0 330 32341 5
Designed by Vidal da Hemp
Phototypeset by Intype, London
Printed by Eagle Colourbooks,
Scotland

To get the leg over all you need is a willing partner. The difficulty here is not finding one, but convincing her that it is a good idea.

Trouble is, most of us willies are born attached to total and utter idiots who have no idea how to go about it. That's why I hope this book may be of some help.

The majority of men are sex maniacs and very EASY. Women find this irritating because unlike men they prefer a challenge. But understandably, men think its an absurd concept to spend their lives chasing something and then play hard to get when they catch up with it.

OOPS, I CAME TOO SOON!

This happens to real enthusiasts but usually when the girl is a shade too pretty. It's frustrating for her, but the condition can be helped if he does algebra in his head while in the leg over situati

# THE WIMP IN YOU

A minority of men are very lucky. They are rich and handsome and get their leg over so often they have to take a holiday every other week to recuperate. Enough about them. (Bastards!)

Leg-over Blindness

A sad condition where men are simply not interested in women. Of course, some men prefer men, as some women prefer women; but that's not what we're talking about here.

No, what we mean is the a-sexual, zero interest syndrome. Like not a flicker even if Roseanna Arquette was wheeled in spread-eagled on a serving trolley.

Young Willie spends so much of his life in the confined surroundings of school shorts that he escapes the conditioning his owner has to endure during his formative years. Environment plays a huge part in forming sexual attitudes, and in later years Willie simply has no idea why the idiot has to make a federal case out of what should be a straightforward leg-over opportunity.

## Want to do it but can't?

You know that feeling when the girl you've been chasing for months suddenly says OK and jumps naked into your bed and something goes ping in your brain and Willie goes fast asleep?

You do?

My God! See a specialist immediately! If impotence is caught within the first three days it can be curable. The main thing is not to worry about it.

## Legovaphobia

If you are a brand manager or have had a strange religious upbringing you could, despite being sex mad, hold back when confronted with it, rather like a spaniel chasing a cornered cat. This is caused by a noxious mixture of stupidity and guilt, and the prognosis is poor.

Psychotherapy isn't going to help because all psychotherapists suffer from legovaphobia. It is endemic to their profession.

Concern for the planet while commendable, tends to dull the libido. This is due to the fact that green is the colour associated with 'Willie Flu' and trips to the clinic.

# THE D.I.Y. FACTOR

Unless you are an amazing contortionist it is impossible to get your leg over yourself.

Even so, there are those who prefer sex with themselves and admit that while it is hardly a leg-over situation, it is still a lot of fun. In fact many come to regard leg-over as a poor substitute.

D.I.Y. sex, let's not be coy – we are talking about masturbation, jerking off... there, we've said it, and so what? D.I.Y. is perfectly normal. A filthy dirty habit – but perfectly normal. An estimated 100% of all people do it which is well above average, and it goes to show what a filthy dirty lot we are.

Side effects include insanity, blindness and ultimately, death.

# BEGGING FOR REJECTION

There are, believe it or not, those among us who are scared stiff of women, and deliberately act in an uncouth way to put them off. Rather than wait for rejection they wade right in and grab rejection on their own terms.

Being a rejectee requires little expertise. All you need is a lot of beer, heavy boots and to shout and fart a lot.

The irony is that women are not scary until you get to know them really well. More about that later.

Other ways to make sure of getting the brush off are:

- Being too bossy.
- Chuckling to yourself.
- Falling pathetically in love.
- Being notoriously fickle.
- Having a willie that's way too big even for the greediest girls.

# DO ANXIETIES WORRY YOU?

Life is too serious to be taken seriously, so if you ever get that feeling that you don't quite have what it takes, laugh it off because you'll be dead soon anyway.

## Age

Younger men worry about getting old and older men worry about being old and the prospect of losing interest in the whole concept of leg-over. But there is no truth in the undeniable fact that as you advance in years you no longer want it. Of course you want it. Haven't you heard of dirty old men?

The problem is <u>doing</u> it. But luckily it's the kind of problem that goes away if you throw money at it.

## Size

No woman actually cares how long your willie is unless she is rich enough not to have anything else to care about. As a rule she has more serious priorities, like the width of your wallet.

Youth

What's the big deal about being young anyway? After the age of six no woman of taste wants to go near you for ten years. And rightly so.

So forget youth pills and look forward to the male menopause, which is when the real fun starts.

# POSITIVE THINKING WORKS

Everybody likes an optimist unless of course he is clearly off his rocker. But the attitude of the old guy on his death bed who took a turn for the nurse is what we should all be aiming for.

Most successful leg-over candidates are men of a cheerful outgoing disposition. Ah, I hear you say, but what about those women who can't resist the depressive and tortured artist? Well screw them, they've all got small tits anyway.

Positive thinkers can take 'no' for an answer, and instead of making a damn fool of themselves, simply ask someone else to dance.

So be enthusiastic. Hope for the best, expect the worst and you'll get some nice surprises.

# CHAPTER 2: WOMEN WITHOUT WHOM...

The first thing to know about women is that they have cornered the market on pussy. They own 100% of it and know exactly how desperate you are to get your hands on some.

It's very fortunate that they don't own all the other life-giving commodities like the air we breathe and the beer we drink, or our very survival would be seriously at risk.

Nice girls however don't let the power they wield go to their heads and are surprisingly helpful throughout negotiations. Some, on the other hand, instead of sharing their wonderful gift use it as a currency to bargain with. Not all that surprising really.

## PENIS ENVY

Ignore Freud, there is no such thing. Women can get as many penises as they want, with no problem. The problem is that they dont seem to want all that many.

Women fall into two categories. The ones you want and the ones you get. This is because the ones you want don't actually exist outside your filthy mind, even in Hollywood.

THINGS YOU DON'T WANT TO OVERHEAR

Well its a bit on the small side — still it goes nicely with his brain

More baby oil, please!!

# THE SEX BETWEEN THE DIFFERENCES

The difference between men and women is so fundamental we could live on different planets (which if we did would rule out any plans for getting the leg over).

Let's say a strange girl puts her hand down the front of a man's pants and gives his best friend a little tweak. What does he do, scream RAPE? No, he smiles and goes into a trance.

If he did it to her, he'd be in all the papers and banged up in prison. It really is a <u>very</u> big difference.

Women are sex-objects and men are meal-tickets. The thin veneer of society tries to obscure this atavistic truth but with little success.

The cave dwellers started the trend and even now, in spite of all the discussion, its rare to see a woman picking up the lunch tab.

So now when Ms. Sex-Object meets the Mr. Meal-Ticket of her dreams it's straight to the Savoy Grill then off to bed (but not on the first date).

That's it, bread and bed, and always in that order because in this corner of the Galaxy women call the shots, darn 'em.

The fact that men are such pushovers is a thing women find very annoying. It means they can't trust them out of their sight, without first neutralising them with an excess of leg-over.

# WHAT IRRITATES WOMEN

Leg-over candidates should be aware of the things that women can't stand about men, and adjust their behaviour accordingly. This may sound cynical, but men are not inclined to be idealists when it comes to sex, and will do or say anything to make sure their leg gets over.

So here is a list of things found to be non-aphrodisiac.

- Secret jokes with your mates.
- Calculated vagueness.
- Indifferent commitment.
- Rational discussion.
- Using foul language other than when making love.
- Comments like 'Reality is a hypothesis' and 'Get married? You must be joking.'
- Getting a pet rattlesnake for Christmas.

The list could be longer, but these are a few of the more obvious turn-offs. Some women have even been known to dislike pinkies in the bum cleavage while in the final stages of a leg-over situation, but they're just weird.

# DANGER, DIFFICULT WOMEN

Women secretly envy men's casual and liberated attitude to sex, because they are trapped in the accepted behaviour of their gender. Thank God. Can you imagine how dreadful it would be to have predatory and sex-obsessed females in your office? You can't? Nor can I, come to think of it.

Lemon faces

Lemon-faced women are never happy no matter how many take-away Chinese dinners you treat them to. Signs to look for:
Does her face look like a lemon? Then she probably is a lemon face. Has she got a terrific body? Then if she's a lemon face it's a terrible shame.
Does she look like a Pekingese licking piss off a stinging nettle? Yes? Then she's a typical L.F.

Masochistic men go for the lemon face and are rarely disappointed.

# P.M.S.-BAD FOR HER, EVEN WORSE FOR YOU

There is a thing called P.M.S. which is short for Pre-Menstrual Syndrome. This can make women very unpredictable and ratty. If she has this it is better to stay out of her way. Just as neo-concepts like 'Jet Lag' and 'Nervous Breakdown' have become accepted as the norm, she will pretend to have P.M.S. even if she hasn't, just for the hell of it.

Needless to say, the condition is leg-over unfriendly so you'll need to make other arrangements.

P.M.S. rarely lasts for more than two days, but if it regularly lasts for over a month then take the hint and move on.

Another neat trick is to complain non-stop that their tits/bum/knees are too big/small/fat/thin. Then say 'Yuk, how could you fancy me?' And when you assure them that you do, they say 'Well you'd fancy anything.'

They tell their friends the size of your willie.

They tell you they don't go out with you for your money then blackmail you into spending it all.

# WOMEN MEN WANT

What men find attractive is a constant source of amazement to women.

Is it the skinny tall model with the fine bone structure? Is it the mysterious pale-faced girl with the chestnut hair and the black baggy outfit?

Nope. If women really knew what was titillating the willie region they'd have a heart attack. Men have simple and uncomplicated minds. Fashion means nothing to us. What brings a lump to our Y-fronts is the bimbo in the tight frock and the diamante jewellery.

Sexy is:

- Anything that gives us a stiffy.
- Pissed and willing.
- Anything we haven't already had.
- Fat girls with dirty eyes.
  (Really fat is when they sit on your face and block out the sound of the stereo.)

Actually all the above is a pack of lies, well not lies exactly, but a gross exaggeration. But at least it acts as a sort of pointer if you're wondering whether or not to wear make-up and high heels.

# CHAPTER 3: JUST LOOKING

All men love with their eyes. We all know what sexy is. We can all spot a 'Yummie' a mile away and we have been known to fall off buildings and out of trains doing so. Girl spotting can be very dangerous for many and varied reasons.

The perfect girl is a strange phenomenon sent just for you and me from the big dating agency in the sky. She is the girl other women describe variously as a 'tart', 'obvious' or 'passée'.

With a write-up like that you know she is right up your alley and that you'd like to be up hers.

She is usually unfashionably dressed in high heels and seamed stockings. She has it and she flaunts it. If you say you don't want one like this you are either a liar or both.

But the chances are you won't get one and will have to settle for a nice normal woman. But you can still dream, and all said and done, it is a spur to get out there and earn lotsa money.

Checklist of desirable qualities:

- Cheerfulness
- Likes you.
- Likes leg-over.
- Likes it often.
- Even in the morning.
- Wants to make you happy.
- Looks astounding.
- Is not cross when you fall asleep afterwards.
- Is fluent in sixteen languages and can't say 'no' in any of them.

Generally speaking women with these qualities can only be found in the East. So if you don't live in Yarmouth you may have to go in for something more realistic.

A girl who wears mens shoes is not sexy. Nor is one who wears dirty overalls – unless she is painting your place in which case she is unbelievably attractive.

Success is getting what you want, happiness is wanting what you get and experience is what you get when you don't get anything

# ARE YOU WHAT SHE WANTS?

Looking for leg-over, on the prowl, tail chasing, or whatever you want to call it, is not the most edifying activity. Never look obvious or desperate or you'll end up empty handed.

So even if you *are* desperate, (and let's face it, you are) at least try to look cool and casual.

Before you get too demanding take a look in a mirror. Are you fat and pimply? Ugly and bald and poorly dressed? Are you a walking rubbish tip? Are you badly behaved? Do your feet smell? Do you have halitosis that could kill a gorilla?

Are you old? Do you have warts on your willie? Or is your willie a wart? Are you a criminal?

If the answer to any of the above is 'yes' then you will be pleased to know that you will probably only appeal to very beautiful women. They're perverse like that.

Few women like macho violent men. The ones that do can be found most nights in the casualty department of your local hospital.

A man who is insulting about women is usually deeply insecure and has to bring them down to his level before he can cope, as in 'The guy who can't dance says the band is lousy.'

Don't use bad language unless requested to do so. Above all, don't get drunk. Get _her_ drunk, by all means.

# LEG-OVER DRESSING

You should try to look your best. The only time you don't have to look your best is when in the 'do it yourself' mode, a subject touched upon earlier.

What to wear is a matter of taste but for men trousers are highly recommended for the early stages, but can be discarded when you gain confidence and a leg-over situation seems to be on the cards.

Whatever you wear under your trousers is a bit hit or miss. You may be lucky and be wearing Y-fronts on the very day you get intimate with a woman with a passion for Y-fronts.

More often than not however the girl you're with won't like your choice of underpants, so do remember to put on several pairs of different types just in case. Very cool.

T-shirts are popular these days. They usually have a message on the front and you will find that you can use these as a way of communicating without actually having to open your mouth. A T-shirt that says, for example, 'HARD DICK, EASY LAY' will give her a clear idea that you are a direct uncomplicated sort of bloke and a complete prat.

Ties are smart, and can be used to good effect to tie her to the bed. You will need four for this, but never wear more than one at a time or you'll look like a fool. The other three can be hidden inside your pink baseball hat, along with your mouth-organ, chewing-gum and other accessories.

Final tip on ties: muted pastel colours are more likely to go with her nightie.

A jacket is a man's second-best friend. It too has places to put things and is the counterpart of a woman's handbag. Do not do hand-stands in it. Jackets must be baggy so there is plenty of room for your Uzi, and even more importantly, your wallet.

# DO'S AND DON'TS

Before you make up your mind that leg-over is definitely the way forward and that you won't become a Trappist monk after all, you should be aware of some of the slings and arrows of outrageous behaviour.

Firstly, do remember that women are only human and although you are looking for perfection, you can't keep her in a cupboard for your personal use, and turn her on and off like a stereo every time you want to make sweet music.

Once you have attracted a girl she will probably turn out to be embarrassingly loyal and only a cad would exploit this uniquely feminine characteristic.

Once the thrill of your first encounter wears off (like the next day) it is common for men to become less enthusiastic. So remember, 'A girl isn't just for Christmas.'

The early worm catches the bird

To avoid involvement some men pay for sex. Women would never do this. They'd sooner spend the money on shoes, and having the car repaired. It's true though that sex you pay for is far cheaper than sex for free.

③ So I had an idea! Play him at his own game! Treat him as a sex-object nothing more

Good!

④ Now he says I'm the most perfect woman he ever met!

Does he give evening classes?

EVERY USEFUL LESSON IN LIFE IS LEARNT A FEW SECONDS TOO LATE FOR IT TO BE USEFUL

# NEEDS AND DON'T NEEDS

You will need a wallet. Wallets, for the best effect, should be bulky and stuffed full of cash, credit cards and photos of your wife. Thin wallets do not impress women and the keen leg-overist should bear this firmly in mind at all times.

Money is very helpful. For some reason women seem to like it, and once the wheels of the leg-over machine have been set in motion, money can be the perfect lubricant.

Remember, good looks, youth and talent are only a substitute for money. Money on the other hand is a substitute for everything.

Go through the checklist of things you need before you get started. It's very embarrassing to discover you're short of an essential when you're already up and running.

Money, cheque-book, credit cards, tooth brush, good looks, youth, talent. If you find you are short of one of these, get it now.

A hotel chain and a Ferrari are useful assets, but only essential if you are aiming high.

She will want romance, entertainment, money, cheque-book, credit cards etc., marriage and children.

A good safeguard against the latter is to be already married, so if you can arrange this all well and good. But remember, be single-minded, particularly if you are married.

Don't be pushy. The softly softly approach works better. Never thrust your hand down her dress until you know her better, like after the third drink.

# CHAPTER 4: CLOSING IN

Let's face it, getting your leg over is a lot sexier than thinking about getting your leg over, which up till now is all you've been doing.

By now your willie will be pointing firmly in the direction of someone you really like the look of, and so long as you are not a freak, it should only be a matter of time before the grand opening ceremony. But of course, it does require a certain amount of action on your part.

It is not enough to stand around looking pretty, particularly if you are ugly. You have to make a move. The face to face approach is favoured by the experts, but the chances are that you will be somewhere where the music is so loud she won't hear a word you're saying and say 'No thanks' just to be on the safe side.

A phone call is probably better, because she won't see you blushing and sweating.

Just pick up the phone and do it. Don't be afraid of making a prat of yourself. When she answers don't chicken out and go 'Click'.

And don't say: 'Hi, this is Dan. I noticed your tits and can I buy them dinner tonight?'

She will not realise this is merely a Freudian slip, and will think you're trying to be funny.

The three things wrong with the above are the words 'tits', 'buy' and 'tonight'. The word 'buy' is vulgar, since it implies that you're trying to appeal to the venal side of her nature which is insulting.

Be more vague: 'Hi, this is Dan. Would you care to join me for dinner?' If she says, 'OK. Like when?' you say 'As soon as possible, preferably every night.' This will either charm her or bring on a dialling tone, but you gotta take chances in this life.

# THE DREADED FIRST DATE

First dates are more stressful than anything known to man.

Look at it this way:

- Do you have to smell nice and turn up on time to get mugged?
- Do you have to look your best in a plane crash?
- Do you have to be suave and charming when your house burns down?
- Do you have to be witty when the stock market wipes you out'

Of course you don't. But how about on that first date?

The thing is to be yourself. However, if you are a complete klutz it's better to be someone else.

Below is a list of things best left out of your chat-up patter, unless, that is, you are desperate for rejection.

- "You're not fat."
- "My wife and I are having a trial separation."
- "Ever considered a breast implant?"
- "My last girlfriend was on the cover of Cosmo in a swimsuit, but don't worry, I'm not into looks any more."
- "I don't suppose anyone has told you you're beautiful before?"
- "My piles are killing me, but you know what it's like."

# LEG-OVER AND LOVE

When you first see a person you want to get your leg over, it is quite common to get a weird fixation about them. It is usually called 'falling in love'.

Recently scientists and forensic chemists have taken over what was once the domain of song writers and poets, and are trying to analyse love and disentangle it from its uncouth bedmate 'lust'.

Some cynics claim that love and lust are one and the same, and although they may be right they'll never get their leg over anyone nice, and serve them right.

Sure, lust does come into the picture a bit ... well ... quite a lot in fact. But it is not the whole picture ... well ... not always anyway.

Love and romance are generally more popular concepts with women than with men, but once you get into the swing of it, you will find the game very enjoyable.

Gifts of flowers and poetry always go down very well and when mixed with a little chocolate and a lot of charm you would have to have very bad breath indeed not to succeed.

But don't play with romance. It is very bad behaviour to tell someone you love them if you don't, just to get your leg over.

Remember, love is a Rottweiler that everyone wants to pet. You <u>can</u> get away with it, but it's a risk.

Love is like measles. The older you are the more serious it is

# BOOZE

Drinking is a way of life in this country as in most others, and in moderation can be a great aphrodisiac.

In those countries where alcohol is banned, leg-over is only practised when offspring are required, and as a result these places tend to be densely populated.

It is said that drink dulls the sexual appetite, but this of course is nonsense unless you drink a helluva lot in which case it's true.

Pouring a small quantity of alcohol down a female throat can do quite remarkable things to her libido, but like everything else it is a mistake to overdo it.

With men, it is important to know your limits, because after a certain amount Willie gets his pyjamas on and goes bye-byes and nothing that either of you can do will wake him.

So, a bottle of wine over dinner is a perfect way to get relaxed and mellow and a hand on the thigh. A brandy with your coffee can get that top button undone. But two more beers gets you a knee in the groin.

# MORE BOOZE

How much alcohol?

Men: Modern medical thinking has put the amount at 201 units, to be spaced sensibly throughout the day. (a unit equals one measure of whisky or a bottle of beer). Women: roughly the same.

Dangers

It would be irresponsible of us not to point out the dangers of alcohol, particularly when on the road.

If you have been drinking, and are on the road, please try to get up. Many a reveller has been squashed flat by a passing truck and they only have themselves to blame.

Drinking and driving

Drinking can seriously impair driving skills and vice versa. Lots of accidents have been caused by the driver holding a bottle in one hand while trying to steer with the other.

It is essential to keep both hands free, one for the wheel and one for your friend's inner thigh. The bottle can be held between the knees, or alternatively, she can hold it in her other hand.

Looking out for the police is also a dangerous distraction, brought on by drinking. Try to keep both eyes focused on the two white lines in the middle of the road.

# DON'T BE DIRTY

Just as things start looking good and you're firing on all cylinders and the leg-over seems so close you can feel its breath, what happens?

Right. Flushed with over-confidence, thinking it's in the bag, you say something dirty or stupid, and end up with a handbag in your ear.

So whatever you're thinking, keep it to yourself, unless they are really nice thoughts and we all know they probably aren't.

# LEG-OVER BOOBY TRAPS

A lot of bad things can happen to the single-minded leg-overist as he goes about his rightful, proper and natural business. This is because his intended victim is usually a woman and women have a whole mindboggling list of wants and don't wants before leg-over can occur.

Among the long list of prior requirements are style, urbanity, intelligence, sensitivity, power, influence, assurance, insurance and a nice car. Oh ... and love.

Even if you are unusual and have some of these, leg-over may not occur until at least the third date. So the whole thing is no doddle.

## Coping with rejection

Come on, own up, you're used to it. Men have the ability to shrug off rejection inbuilt into their D.N.A. This comes from centuries of saying the wrong thing and getting the elbow.

Call us old fashioned, but when we say 'date' we mean D.A.T.E. date! Dinner... drinks... disco... bed... sex... the lot!

Coping with acceptance

This is a really tricky one, because it comes as such a big surprise. A stiff drink is helpful, and then on to the next stage.

What did I say?

THINGS YOU DON'T WANT TO HEAR ON A FIRST DATE

• Mummy is dying to meet you
• It's so nice to go out with someone who doesn't mind I used to be a man.
• Yes, I'm six months pregnant. I'm really surprised you didn't notice.

My last boyfriend had a teensy weensy one. Couldn't have been more than about 7 inches

If I ran a company I wouldn't put you in charge of new business

# CHAPTER 5: DOING IT

And now for the hard part

Well congratulations, here you are at her place, with a throbbing animal down your trousers and a bemused smile on your face.

Now what? Well, while she's making coffee you can make a mental checklist of all the doors and windows in case her husband or boyfriend suddenly shows up.

The first move takes a little courage, but you've gotta make it now or you'll become too friendly and leg-over will no longer be on the menu.

Girls like a gentle and tender approach, so don't shove both hands down the front of her dress. One hand is quite enough and it leaves the other free for your cigar.

Kissing is the most intimate thing two people can do, and it is also good fun. And if either or both of you are ugly it gets you close enough not to notice.

There are 291 sex positions but after 118 You'll need a partner

KAMA SUTRA

ORAL SEX

If you find yourself with strange symptoms such as lacerated tongue, lock-jaw, neck-ache, impaired vision, loss of hearing or crushed skull, and don't know why, the chances are it's from oral sex.

It's great, but you can over-do it, so always consult a physician first.

Warming up excercises and training techniques involve bending forward at 90° placing your face on the wall and putting all your weight on it for as long as possible.

In bed as everywhere else we are very different. She wants three hours of foreplay, three orgasms, a cigarette then start all over again. He wants one minute of foreplay, one orgasm, one beer and one hour's sleep. And when he's ready to start again he gets upset because she's gone off the boil.

To keep him in a sexual frenzy it helps to wear trashy underwear.

Packaging is important – and remember high-heeled sandals are not for walking in. Just take them off along with your make-up when you get up in the morning.

# LEG-OVER TECHNIQUE

It is generally felt that the 'no technique' technique is the best way. Do what feels right and natural. Of course there's always the chance that she might object to this and insist you remove the vibrator.

REGULAR MAINTENANCE RELIEVES STIFF JOINTS

## JEALOUSY

a.k.a. The green eyed monster it is reckoned to be even worse than the pink monster.

They've known each other three weeks and here's us meeting for the very first time!

Seen one seen 'em all

## TECHNO-SEX

WOMEN OFTEN COMPLAIN ABOUT MALE SEXUAL RESPONSES BEING TOO MECHANICAL, AS IF IT WERE ALL A MATTER OF PRESSING THE RIGHT BUTTONS

PLAY

F. FWD

PAUSE

STOP

REWIND

EJECT

As you gradually get to know one another you will begin to realise that there are more ways to do it than the doggy position.

Whole new vistas will open up to you. For example, if you can bear the sight of each other you can experiment and try it face to face, with her lying on her back, and you on top. This is called the 'missionary position' and many couples, once they have got over the initial shock, do it this way most of the time.

Oral sex is a unique thrill and even if you are not feeling hungry you will soon work up an appetite.

Sixty-nine (soixante-neuf) is when you both indulge at once, and it is a wonderful shared experience even if it does tend to rule out small talk.

Well, that's about as vulgar as we are going to get on this page. Just remember there are lots of terrific things you can do and the fun is discovering them together.

Wait till you try taking all your clothes off and leaving all the lights on! You'll never look back.

We have a terrible relationship. He never asks me what I like!

# SAFE SEX

The main drawback of safe sex is finding a safe big enough to accommodate the two of you. And there's always the danger the door might slam shut.

Just kidding. What we are really talking about is contraception. The main purpose of these products is to avoid pregnancy.

The safest form of contraception is the 'withdrawal' method. The moment she gets that suggestive gleam in her eye, he withdraws to the other room and hits the port decanter, but hopefully not hard enough to break it.

It is also quite common practice to withdraw while actually engaged in a leg-over situation. About ten minutes before her orgasm and a split second before his, he removes his willie and gloops all over the duvet. Yuk!

The condom is for people who don't like sex anyway, and who can only get off on the smell of burning rubber.

Condoms come in all kinds of flavours and three different sizes: 'Big' (small), 'Gigantic' (normal) and 'Jesus Christ' (speaks for itself). The flavours are lemon, strawberry, plain and tuna. Willie hates condoms, particularly the ones with lumps on.

The pill is the safest method until it eventually kills you. It works very well, but is unsuitable for the more 'experienced' woman as it can keep falling out.

The diagram is used by some women even though they usually don't know what it's a diagram of. In these circumstances it is wise to view it through half-closed eyes from a distance of several feet. Rubber again, it can cause endless fun when it slips from the fingers during insertion and whammies off the wall, turning your bathroom into a kind of small squash court.

# SAFE ... ISH SEX

Vasectomy is foolproof if you can find anyone foolish enough to believe you've had the operation. The technique was invented by the Turks in 93 BC and was a painful and crude affair, in those days having less to do with contraception and more to do with forcibly gaining information.

The modern operation is more humane, although there are still some side effects such as watering of the eyes and a meeting of the eyebrows above the nose.

The coil or I.U.D. was discovered accidentally by a district nurse while practising trampoline techniques on an old wire-spring bedstead in her garage. She is reported to have said at the time, 'I'll never do that again.' She hasn't.

SEX AND RELIGION

DID YOU KNOW:
- In parts of Africa the 'Missionary Position' is still a capital offense.
- In the Third World sex starvation is widespread despite airlifts in giant transport planes of pornographic videos.
- Strict Catholics who wish to wear a condom can now do so provided they first cut the end off with a pair of sharp scissors.

A strawberry flavoured condom?? I hate strawberries!

They were out of cheese and onion

NO LEG-OVER HANDBOOK WOULD BE COMPLETE WITHOUT ACKNOWLEDGING AIDS. THERE, WE ACKNOWLEDGED IT.

SERIOUSLY THOUGH AIDS IS A SCOURGE AND CLAIMS LIVES. THE CYNICS AMONG US WILL SAY, SURE, BUT PEOPLE DIE FROM CHOKING ON WHOLEMEAL BREAD OR FROM SPRINTING UP MOUNTAINS. THE POINT THEY ARE MISSING IS THAT THOSE TWO ACTIVITIES ARE NEITHER MUCH FUN NOR A BURNING SOCIAL ISSUE.

AIDS IS THOUGHT TO SPREAD BY GETTING YOUR LEG OVER IN THE DARK, WHILE DRUNK AND GETTING HOPELESSLY LOST.

THE CLEAR MESSAGE IS, REMEMBER TO ALWAYS WEAR A CONDOM EACH TIME YOU EMBARK ON A NEW WHOLEMEAL SANDWICH.

Familiarity breeds children

# WEIRD LEG-OVER

A failing sex urge or loss of libido can prompt you to spice up your sex life with things that would be a little out of the ordinary if everyone wasn't doing it. Weird leg-over is what keeps millions of relationships and sex shops alive and kicking.

A lot of people like getting tied up, dressed up, hung up and even beaten up. It is extraordinary the lengths they will go to, to avoid the straightforward leg-over scene.

It is for you alone to figure out what fantasy turns you on most, but getting started or talking about it can be embarrassing. You feel such a fool asking her to dress up as a traffic warden and stick a parking ticket in your bum cleavage.

Better you should both write down a list of twelve wild fantasies and then roll a pair of dice to decide which one you are going to do. That way you can find yourself in bed with her, her best friend, a bunch of grapes, a jar of honey, and a wooden spatula.

### KINKS IN HISTORY

Katherine the Great was killed in a horse riding accident. The horse was riding her, but subsequently got off on a technicality

What can I say?

Drugs can be an intriguing addition to your leg-over routine. They can have some pretty weird and unusual effects depending on what type you go in for. Most interesting drugs are illegal of course, but you can do anything you like with standard aspirin-based analgesics, antacids and hair conditioners, and still stay within the bounds of the law.

Very disappointing though is more or less anything you can buy in a sex shop, because when you get it home, ten to one you've forgotten the batteries.

The strangest perversions of all are 1. celibacy and 2. marriage. (See over.)

# LEG-OVER IN WEDLOCK

Sounds like some painful wrestling hold, which indeed it is.

There comes a point where she offers you guaranteed leg-over for life and at the time it seems like a great idea. So you turn dalliance into drama and get married.

Some men, blind to the incredible financial advantages of having a mistress, keep getting married, presumably to fulfil a lemming-like urge to continually subdivide their wealth until one day they wake up with nothing.

Ironically it is at this point a wife, for the first time ever, would be useful.

99% of marriages are perfectly happy, but it's on the way back from the ceremony the trouble seems to start. Even so, marriage can show two people what real happiness is, but by then of course it's too late.

Marriage is when you touch her hand, look at her with that special look you save for those times you look at her in that special way, and whisper, 'Hey, guess what we're going to do the moment we finish dinner'... and she says 'Yeah, the dishes.'

Divorce is horribly expensive, but at least you'll get to really know each other in a way you never did before.

# DOING IT WHEN YOU CAN'T

The male menopause will probably
be the best time of your life,
chasing girls and spending all
your money, but after that what?

Can you still get it on when
you're getting on? Can you be a
'toy dirty old man'?

Sure. All you need is a great deal
of money. If you don't have any,
get some. If you can't get some
hang up your libido and forget it.

Older people get all kinds of
anxieties about leg-over. Don't. It's
undignified. Just try to picture
yourself doing it . . . Not nice.

So just stop, and take up
something more sedate like hang
gliding or rock climbing.

Who wants to die of old age?

When you're old
enough to afford
anything you want
you don't want it

# Contents

## LEGEND OF APOLLO

Feel the impact of a Saturn V rocket launch, be part of a Moon landing and discover the smell of space in **Legend of Apollo** at our 4D cinema. Located on the ground floor of the Wellcome Wing.

THIS BOOK BELONGS TO

# Weird and Wonderful

The Museum contains some very unusual objects – can you find any of the ones pictured here? Have a good look in all the galleries and **tick the boxes** when you find them.

*If you want some help, the floors you need are on page 46!*

## Banshee

The Banshee is a pilotless aircraft flown under radio control, or using its own autopilot and navigation system on a pre-programmed route. It's used as a target for military training.

## The original Orrery

This beautiful model was commissioned by the Earl of Orrery in 1712 and was one of the first mechanical models of the solar system ever made. Turning the handle shows the movements of the Sun, Earth and the Moon in one day.

> What do you get if you put a clock on the Moon?
> **A luna-tick!**

## Bleadon Man

A 2,000-year-old skeleton was found in Bleadon, Somerset. This reconstruction of the face was built by medical artist Caroline Wilkinson. She used her knowledge of facial muscles to recreate the face, but had to guess what his hair might have looked like.

## Clothes from carpet

This dress, designed by fashion legend Vivienne Westwood, is made entirely from carpet! It weighs 15 kg and had to be specially softened to manipulate it into shape. Designed in the 1990s, the dress resembles the kind of style once worn by Queen Elizabeth I in the 16th century.

## The clever Klein bottle

In 1882 a German mathematician called Felix Klein came up with the idea of an object with only one surface. Called the Klein bottle, the surface has no edge and no identifiable 'inside' or 'outside'. The Klein bottle can be 'cut' in certain ways to form two Möbius strips.

## The bubble car

The Isetta 'bubble car' was first produced in 1953 and started off a trend for these little bubble-shaped vehicles. The car had a single front-opening door. It could reach a maximum speed of 55 mph.

## One-million-volt particle accelerator

Part of a particle accelerator designed by John Cockroft and Ernest Walton. It generated 1.25 million volts to accelerate protons and smash them into atomic nuclei, breaking the nuclei apart. During World War II this machine contributed to the Manhattan Project, which created the first atomic bombs. Cockcroft and Walton's work earned them a Nobel Prize.

### Did you know?

To make a Möbius strip, cut a strip of paper, give it a half-twist, then tape the ends together. You'll find you have a surface with only one side and one edge, no front or back, no beginning and no end. What happens if you draw a line around the strip? Now try cutting along the line you've drawn – what do you get?

## The 'baked bean' telescope

Phil Shepherdson was only 18 when he designed and built this home-made reflecting telescope. That's unusual, but what's really unique is the fact that he made it from everyday objects – including several baked bean cans and wire coat hangers!

### How did you do?

**1-3**  Not bad, but there is still loads more to see – keep those eyes peeled!

**4-6**  A pretty good effort – why not try finding the ones you missed on your next visit!

**7-8**  You are a scientific Super Spotter – do you fancy a job here?

# Things to do at the Museum

## Launchpad (third floor)

You'll have a blast in **Launchpad** – a hands-on, brains-on gallery that will really make you think about the world around you. If you've got a question, look out for an Explainer – they're the ones wearing orange T-shirts.

**Launchpad** is divided into six sections:

- **Light:** Experiment with all kinds of reflections, colour mixing and shadows.
- **Materials:** See how soap makes water 'stretch' and find out about explosions and mixtures.
- **Energy Transfer:** See some spectacular ways in which energy gets transferred.
- **Forces and Motion:** See how science predicts how objects move – then spin like a skater on the Rotation Station!
- **Electricity and Magnetism:** Watch metal floating inside copper and gaze at the beautiful magnetic fields.
- **Sound:** Shout inside a giant echo tube.

Why did the chicken go to **Launchpad**? To do an egg-speriment!

**Younger brothers and sisters will love The Garden and Pattern Pod!**

### The Garden (basement)

An interactive paradise where you can explore everything from water to wobbly towers.

- Enter the wonderful water zone, where you can scoop, pump and pour to your heart's content – but don't forget to pop on an apron as things can get pretty damp!

- In the building zone have a ton of fun exploring materials, transporting objects, building and using tools.

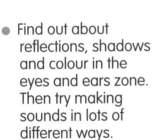

- Find out about reflections, shadows and colour in the eyes and ears zone. Then try making sounds in lots of different ways.

### Pattern Pod (ground floor)

- Explore colourful movement patterns by following light-up footprint trails.
- Make stunning symmetry patterns on computers and see them displayed on a big screen.
- Discover patterns like spirals and hexagons that turn up again and again in everyday things.
- Make water ripple patterns without getting your feet wet.

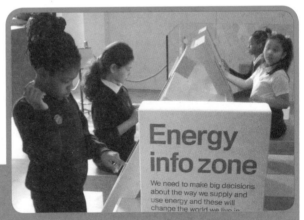

Energy info zone

We need to make big decisions about the way we supply and use energy and these will change the world we live in

### Energy – fuelling the future

**Check out this brilliant gallery (second floor) packed with interactive exhibits:**

- Energy Shutdown is a collection of fun arcade-style games. Help to restore power to a city suffering a blackout!
- Become an Energy Minister and decide how to get power to your people. If you fail, your country will be in the dark…
- Experience energy through touch in the interactive artwork 'Do not touch' by Christian Moeller.
- Be wowed by the thoughts on the Energy Ring, a huge interactive sculpture suspended in the air.

# Exploring Space

**Humans have always looked at the mysterious darkness above them and wondered what could be out there...**

## Quick quiz

What was the first living creature to be launched into space?

a  a dog
b  a monkey
c  a hamster

Answer:

Answer on page 46

## Cramped capsule

In 1969 three astronauts squeezed themselves inside this Apollo 10 capsule on a mission to travel to the Moon and back. The space inside was tiny – about the size of a small car. The mission was successful – and it paved the way for the Apollo 11 Moon landing two months later.

Find me in **Making the Modern World**

## Did you know?

In the entire history of space travel only 12 people have ever stepped on to the Moon.

You can see, hear, feel and smell what it was like to be on one of the Apollo missions with **Force Field**, our motions effect simulation theatre (ground floor). Hold on tight!

## Real rocket science

The **J2 engine** is one of the most important engines in the history of manned space flight. It was used for the powerful **Saturn V rocket**, which launched the Apollo missions to the Moon.

The **Saturn V rocket** was more than 110 metres tall – that's nearly as big as the London Eye.

### Did you know?
Scientists don't know what 90% of the universe is made of.

Find us both in
**Exploring Space**

## Man on the Moon

On 20 July 1969 millions of excited people watched as astronauts Neil Armstrong and Buzz Aldrin took their first steps on to another world. Apollo 11, the first mission to land humans on the Moon, had made history. The astronauts made the last part of their journey in a lunar landing module called the Eagle. As Armstrong stepped on to the Moon's surface, he said the famous words…

### 'That's one small step for man, one giant leap for mankind.'

Fancy watching a rocket taking flight? Then make your way to **Launchpad** (third floor) for the explosive Rocket Show!

What do astronauts play during long missions?
**Moon-opoly!**

WOW! **That's** big!

# Life in Space

## Visiting space has always been a challenge for humans.

### Spacesuit survival

Sending a person into space – and keeping them alive – is very difficult. In space there is no air and extreme temperatures. All that stands between a spacewalking astronaut and this deadly environment is a spacesuit and helmet. The suit has many layers and is specially pressurised to protect the wearer. An oxygen supply helps the astronaut breathe.

### Space station adventurers

We've come a long way since 1969. Humans can now live in space for months at a time – on board the International Space Station (ISS). This amazing craft is currently orbiting the Earth, providing a home for astronauts from around the world. Through their work, we are learning about how humans can live and work in space – perhaps, one day, permanently.

⊙ This suit (in **Exploring Space**) was worn by Helen Sharman, the first British person to go into space, in May 1991.

Why did the astronaut feel hungry?
**Because it was launch time!**

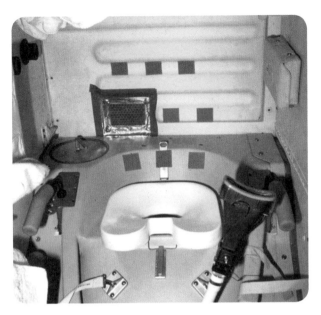

## Astro-nappies!

On Earth, the force of gravity keeps our wee and poo safely in the toilet. But in space there is hardly any gravity, so everything (yes, everything) floats around. The solution is – a special space toilet. Astronauts can also wear disposable 'space nappies', which means they can 'go' on long flights and spacewalks without needing to take off their spacesuits!

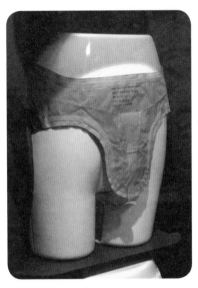

Find the space nappy in **Exploring Space**

**What am I?**

a  a hi-tech transmitter for communicating with aliens

b  a warming plate for heating an astronaut's food

c  a heat-resistant tile that protects the outside of the Space Shuttle

**Answer:**

Answer on page 46

**What would happen if you farted in a spacesuit?**

As your suit is tightly sealed, you couldn't possibly open it to let the fart out – your blood would boil, your internal organs would swell up and finally… you'd freeze! So it would be the worst kind of fart ever: you couldn't deny it, you couldn't escape it, and the smell would stay with you all the way back to the space station.

# Space Investigation

## There is still so much for us to find out…

### Black Arrow

The Black Arrow was Britain's first and only satellite launch vehicle. A Black Arrow R3, 13.1 metres tall (that's bigger than a house), launched the Prospero satellite in 1971, making Britain the fifth nation to launch its own spacecraft. Prospero will continue to orbit the Earth for the rest of the 21st century.

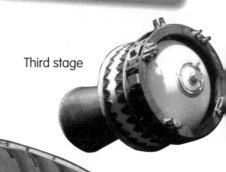

Third stage

Second stage

First stage

### Hubble trouble

A telescope the size of a bus, the Hubble Space Telescope, was put into orbit around Earth in 1990 so it could get clear images of very distant objects. At first it didn't work properly – the images were blurred. It was fixed in 1993 and began to send us amazing pictures like this one of the Eagle Nebula, a famous cluster of stars and star-forming gas.

### Quick quiz

How long does it take the Hubble telescope to orbit the Earth?

a   about 9.5 minutes
b   about 19 hours
c   about 97 minutes

Answer:

Answer on page 46

Find Prospero in
**Exploring Space**

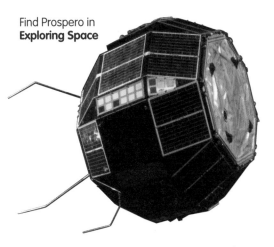

## Surrounded by satellites

The world's first artificial satellite, Sputnik, was launched by the Russians in 1957. Since then thousands of satellites have been launched into orbit around the Earth – it's pretty crowded out there! These satellites help us:

- Keep an eye on Earth's resources and climate change
- Find our way around using satnav
- Watch television (by beaming down signals)
- Forecast the weather

↑ **Prospero** was an experimental satellite, made to test things used all the time in space: solar cells, protective coatings, and remote monitoring and operation of equipment.

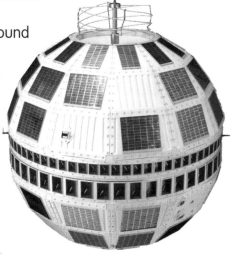

↑ Telstar was the first satellite to receive and transmit live TV around the world.

**Did you know?**
There are about 3,000 artificial satellites orbiting Earth at this very moment. But there are thousands more pieces of space junk up there...

How do you get a baby astronaut to sleep?
**Rock-it!**

## What's it like out there?

We send probes into space to find out about other parts of the solar system. In 1997 the Cassini-Huygens probe was launched on a mission to Saturn and its moon Titan. The probe reached Saturn in 2004 after a 2 billion mile journey. The Huygens lander touched down on Titan using parachutes to land.

**11**

# Steaming Ahead

## Steam power transformed industry and changed people's lives

### Steam changed the world

Until steam came along, we got our power from flowing water, wind, and from animals and human beings. But when Thomas Newcomen developed the first steam engine (around 1712) power became available on a massive scale for the first time.

### Trevithick's Pen-y-darren locomotive

Built in 1804, Richard Trevithick's steam locomotive was the world's first locomotive to successfully haul a load on a railway. It showed that steam could haul a far greater load than a horse.

Find me in
**Making the
Modern World**

### Stephenson's incredible Rocket

**Robert Stephenson built the Rocket for the 1829 Rainhill Trials, a competition to find the best locomotive engine for the new Liverpool and Manchester railway line. Reaching a top speed of 29 mph, the Rocket won to a cheering crowd. The Rocket is now the most famous steam locomotive in the world.**

How do you know if a steam train is happy?
**It looks chuffed!**

Find me in the
**Energy Hall**

## Mighty mill engine

A steam engine like this 1903 model could drive 1,700 power looms at the same time! This kind of engine soon replaced the huge rocking beams of earlier models.

## The downside of steam

Steam power changed everything. Industry was booming and many kinds of goods were being made by the new factories. But life could be hard for the people that worked in them. Working conditions were often dirty and dangerous and the hours were long. Many children worked in the mills and factories and never went to school. Some had to work from early in the morning to late at night, seven days a week. Can you imagine working that hard?

Want to see the mill engine in action? The Science Museum sometimes operates this machine. Ask at the Information Desk for details.

## What am I?

a   a power loom – used for weaving
b   a mangle – for squeezing water out of clothes
c   a printing press – for printing books

Answer:

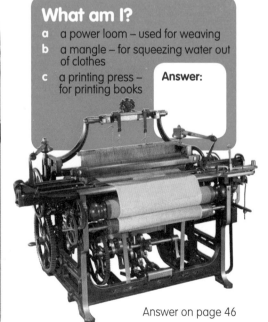

Answer on page 46

## Non-stop across the Atlantic

Alcock and Brown made the first non-stop flight across the Atlantic in this Vickers Vimy biplane in June 1919. They flew from Newfoundland and ended up crash-landing in a bog in Ireland. The Vickers Vimy was a heavy bomber, designed for use during World War I. It was made mainly of wood and had two Rolls-Royce engines.

# Flying Machines

**In 1903 the Wright brothers flew the first successful powered aeroplane – but there have been many other achievements in aviation.**

### Did you know?

The first living creatures to travel in a hot-air balloon were a sheep, a duck and a chicken!

## Balloon crazy

The Montgolfier brothers made the first human flight in history when they took off in their hot-air balloon in November 1783. The balloon flew above Paris on a journey taking 25 minutes. It caused a sensation and a balloon 'craze' soon followed. This souvenir has four perfume bottles inside.

## Silver sensation

The Lockheed Electra first flew in February 1934. This aerodynamic monoplane had features such as supercharged air-cooled wing-mounted engines, a retractable undercarriage and wing flaps.

Fly with the RAF Red Arrows in stunning 3D or take the controls yourself in our 360° flight simulators. Visit **Fly Zone** on the third floor.

Find me in **Making the Modern World**

## Gloster-Whittle E28/39 jet

The first-ever British jet aircraft made its first official flight on 15 May 1941. It had a jet propulsion engine, developed by Frank Whittle. The age of the jet had begun.

Find me in **Flight**

What wobbles as it flies through the air?
**A jelly-copter!**

## Straight up!

The fast, powerful gas turbine engine transformed aviation in the years following World War II. The Hawker P.1127 VSTOL Experimental Aircraft achieved vertical take-off on 21 October 1960.

## World War II wonder

The Spitfire is one of Britain's most famous aircraft. Designed by Reginald G. Mitchell, Spitfires gained their place in history during the Battle of Britain in 1940 when they were used to fight attacking German planes in the skies over southern England.

**15**

# On the Road

Cars and bikes have given us the freedom to travel further and faster.

## Beetling along

Nicknamed for its bug-like shape, the German-produced Volkswagen Beetle became incredibly popular all over the world after World War II. In 1981, the 20 millionth Beetle was produced, beating the 15 million units of the previous best-selling car, the Ford Model T. Beetles are still widely driven today.

**Quick quiz**

The Bugatti Veyron is one of the fastest cars in the world. What is its top speed?

a   about 180 mph
b   about 250 mph
c   about 300 mph

Answer:

Answer on page 46

## Solar-powered racing

The 'Mad Dog' was Britain's most successful solar-powered racing car in the 1990s. It won the Stock Class at the 1998 World Solar Rally in Japan, reaching speeds of over 25 mph – pretty good for a car run on the energy of the Sun!

## The 'penny farthing'

The distinctive 'penny farthing' was the typical bicycle people rode from 1870 till about 1890. The pedals were directly attached to the large front wheel, which helped the rider to go faster.

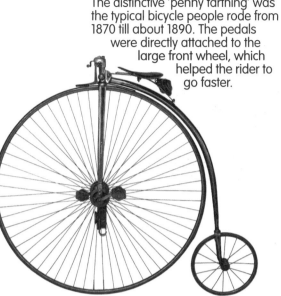

## Chopper crazy

This unusual style of kid's bike was very popular in Britain from the early 1970s. The design was inspired by motorbikers who modified, or 'chopped', their machines to look different.

## The fabulous Ford

**The Ford Model T is one of the world's most well-known cars. It was introduced in 1908 by Henry Ford, and manufactured in large numbers at new Ford factories in the USA. Simple and affordable, the Model T enabled thousands of ordinary people to buy a car for the first time. It had a maximum speed of 40 mph.**

Find us in
**Making the
Modern World**

When is a car
not a car?
**When it turns
into a garage!**

# Ship Ahoy!

**Before air travel, ships and boats enabled us to travel the world.**

## Quick quiz

The sides of a boat are called port and starboard – but which is right and which is left?

**Answer:**

Answer on page 46

Find us all in **Ships**

## Cute coracles

Small bowl-shaped vessels called coracles have been used by fishermen for centuries. Suitable for fast-flowing rivers, coracles are one of the few boats that can be carried on your back once you've made your trip!

What kinds of stories do they tell on board ships?

**Ferry tales!**

## The fastest steamer

The TS Mauretania was a quadruple-screw steamship launched in 1906 for voyages between Liverpool and New York. Mauretania was the fastest ship across the Atlantic for more than 20 years, travelling at speeds of up to 27 knots.

## Did you know?

Viking longboats sailed fastest when they were powered by wind. On a calm day, with 20–30 men rowing, their top speed would only have been about 6 mph – you can run faster than that!

## The Santa Maria

The Santa Maria was the largest of the three sailing ships used by Christopher Columbus on his famous voyage across the Atlantic in 1492 when he discovered the West Indies.

## Deep-sea dives

This heavy diving helmet was used for deep-sea diving in the North Sea by divers looking for oil. Air was pumped down to the diver via a rubber pipe. Weighted boots had to be worn to help keep the diver deep down underwater.

### Did you know?

**The speed of ships and aircraft is measured in knots.**
1 knot = 1.15 miles per hour
1 knot = 1.85 km per hour

## The biggest steamship

The SS Great Eastern, launched in 1858, was the largest ship of her day, able to carry 4,000 passengers around the world. She had steam engines powering a four-bladed screw propellor and two enormous paddle wheels.

The model is pretty big – the actual ship was 100 times bigger!

# Marvellous Medicine

Find me in **Making the Modern World**

**There have been many important medical discoveries and inventions over the years.**

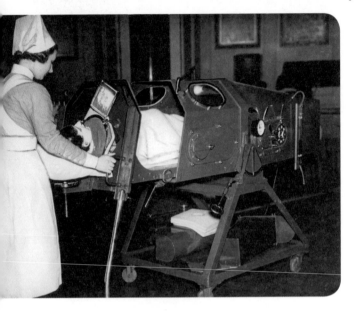

## A life-saving medicine

It's strange to think that penicillin, the first ever antibiotic, is actually made from mould! In 1928 Alexander Fleming discovered that a strain of Penicillium mould produced a substance that killed certain bacteria. It took until the 1940s for the medicine penicillin to become a powerful weapon against many diseases.

## Living in an 'iron lung'

The iron lung was the first ever life-support machine. It was used for children and adults whose chest muscles were paralysed, usually as a result of a terrible disease called polio. The machine snapped shut around the body, leaving only the head free. Inside, a pump sucked the air in and out, keeping the person breathing. Some children spent their whole lives inside the iron lung.

### Did you know?

In the UK, all children are vaccinated against polio when they are babies – though you might not remember!

## New ways of seeing

In the 1970s a new machine called a Magnetic Resonance Imaging scanner was developed. Giant magnets built up pictures based on the magnetic behaviour of water molecules inside the patient's body. The MRI scanner is now widely used in hospitals.

## Bodily parts

Models like this once helped people learn about the human body. This wooden model, with removable organs, was made in the 17th century.

Find me in **The Science and Art of Medicine**

What part of your body has the best sense of humour?
**Your funny bone!**

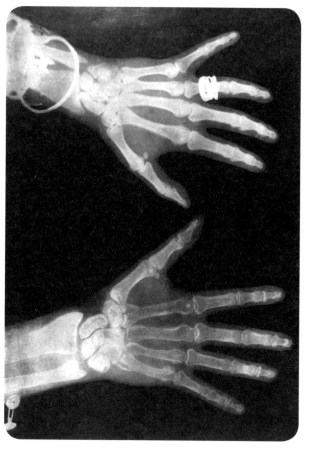

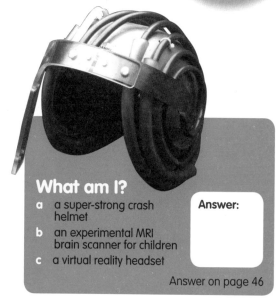

## What am I?

a   a super-strong crash helmet

b   an experimental MRI brain scanner for children

c   a virtual reality headset

**Answer:**

Answer on page 46

## The first X-rays

Though X-rays were first discovered in 1895 by Wilhelm Conrad Röntgen, X-ray machines were rare before World War I. But by the 1930s there was a specialist X-ray department in every UK hospital. Now doctors could see bones and other structures inside the living body.

# Your Amazing Brain

**Everything about you is amazing – but your brain is something really special.**

### Your incredible brain

**People used to believe that their hearts contained all their feelings. But scientists now know that our thoughts, feelings, memories and reason all emerge from 1.5 kg of wrinkled grey flesh – the brain! Our brain is more complex than that of any other species, containing an astonishing 100 billion brain cells.**

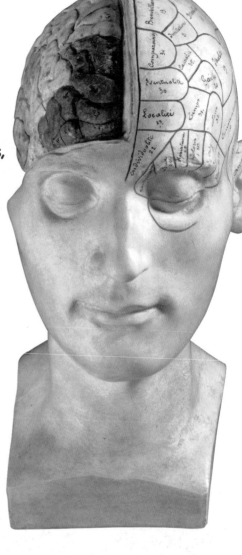

### It's all about connections

But what really makes your brain brilliant is not so much the number of cells but the connections between them. These links – a cool trillion of them – carry information from one area of the brain to another and give you your ability to think, reason and remember.

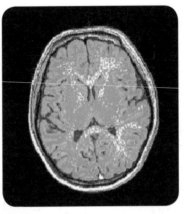

### How do you feel?

Your face can be very revealing. Wrinkling your nose, a smile or a scowl – are you even aware of the look on your face? Although we can choose what expression we wear, often our faces show the emotions we're really feeling.

**Did you know?**

If you clench both fists and put your knuckles together, that's roughly how big your brain is. It's just a lot squishier!

22

## Who are you?

Our brains are programmed to remember thousands of different faces. Even babies can recognise faces! Scientists know this because newborn babies will look at a simple face picture (far left) for longer than a face-like pattern.

Why was the brain afraid of water?

It didn't want to be brain-washed!

Have fun with faces – see if you can guess people's emotions from their facial expressions in **Who am I?**

### Did you know?

No-one knows for certain why we need to sleep, but we do know that sleep is vital for our brains to work properly. The longest that a person has gone without sleep is 11 days!

## Monkey business

Chimps are our closest animal relatives, but their brains are much smaller than ours. This means their reasoning and planning skills are not as advanced as humans'. So don't ask them to assemble furniture or organise a party!

### Quick quiz

Which creature has the heaviest brain?

a  a sperm whale

b  a human

c  an elephant

**Answer:**

Answer on page 47

23

# What Makes You, You?

You have a lot in common with all the people around you – but you are also a completely unique person.

## The same but different

Your brain is shaped by your own experience of life, and the genes that you inherit from your parents make you quite different from anyone else.

## Building blocks of life

DNA is a substance that can be found in almost every cell of the body, where it carries instructions to guide how your body develops. Genes are made up of particular sequences of DNA, and are like tiny pieces of a secret code. Genes are passed on from parents to children, and no two organisms (except clones and identical twins) have the same DNA.

### A white peacock

A variation in this peacock's genes made it grow up with colourless feathers – a very unusual sight. Gene variations are what gives you black, red, curly or straight hair – and what might make you go bald one day!

DNA can be seen under very powerful microscopes. Scientists figured out that it was a double helix shape in 1953.

### Did you know?

You are taller when you get up than just before you go to bed.

### What am I?

a   a device being developed to carry out on-the-spot genetic tests

b   a machine that works out how long you will live

c   a smartphone

Answer:

Answer on page 47

### How do I look?

Do you have your mum's nose? Your dad's long legs or curly hair? Your looks are a product of your genes, from your face-shape to your feet.

## Monster mouse

At the end of a meal, your fat cells send a chemical message to your brain to give the signal that you are full up. Scientists 'turned off' the gene for this signal and so this mouse didn't know when to stop eating!

## The cat with seven toes

Genes govern the number of fingers and toes any creature has. A change in one type of these genes can mean that extra digits may develop. A tiny number of humans and animals are born with extra fingers and toes.

## More than genes

Genes aren't the only factor, however. Your environment and how you live your life are also very important. For example, some of your genes influence whether you are more likely to be fat or thin, muscle-bound or puny. But your body shape also depends a lot on what you eat and the exercise you take.

Why can't cats use a DVD player?

Because they can only press Paws!

## Did you know?

Starfish can regrow their legs if they lose one.

## Could you be rebuilt?

The tiny differences in your DNA that make you unique also influence your health and how long you might live. One day, artificial eyes, tissue transplants grown from your own cells and computer-assisted limbs could quite literally keep you going. Your body could be rebuilt in many different ways – but would you still be you?

# Exciting Energy

## Without energy on tap our lives would be very different.

Energy is vital in our lives. We all need fuel – the food we eat – to keep us alive and power our bodies. And we use huge amounts of energy to keep ourselves warm, and to power our homes, workplaces and cars.

### What are fossil fuels?

Our planet has natural stores of energy, called **fossil fuels** – substances such as oil, coal and gas, which have taken millions of years to form. They are also called non-renewable energy sources, because one day they will run out.

The gases released by burning so much of these fuels are already affecting our climate.

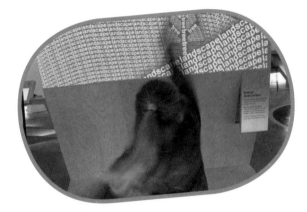

### Did you know?

A bolt of lightning contains enough energy to toast 160,000 pieces of bread. But as it only lasts 0.00001 seconds, turning the bread over might prove difficult!

### Power from the Sun and wind

Solar (from the Sun) and wind power are **renewable** energy sources – as it's unlikely that we'll ever run out of wind, or sunlight. Neither of these methods alone could produce enough energy to meet all our needs. But renewable energy sources could help us use fewer fossil fuels and limit the damage to our planet.

Why is wind power so popular? Because it has a lot of fans!

Get energetic at **Launchpad** (third floor). Can you pedal hard enough to power a light bulb, radio or hairdryer?

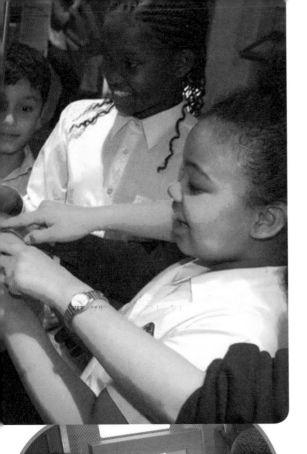

## Poo power!

Scientists are scratching their heads to think of new energy sources that won't hurt the planet. One idea has been to use 'natural waste' – something we all produce every day – as a power source. You've got it – poo!

MOO LOO

The Sun is the source of most of the world's energy

Have fun finding out about energy in the interactive **Energy** gallery (second floor).

## Quick quiz

Every day up to 70 million barrels of oil are pumped out of the ground. How much longer can we keep supplying this amount?

a   3 years
b   30 years
c   300 years

**Answer:**

Answer on page 47

## The things you can do with poo…

● Researchers in Japan are looking at ways to generate hydrogen fuel from cow poo and wee, among other things.

● In Great Britain, there is already a power station which is completely powered by chicken poo!

● People in Denmark can leave out their poo for the bin men to collect – it is recycled to make compost.

● A firm based in Sri Lanka – called 'Mr Ellie Pooh' – produces paper which is partly made from elephant dung.

# Future Earth

### So, how does the future look for our planet?

Our atmosphere is a layer of gases held in place by Earth's gravity. It causes the blue glow around Earth in photos like this.

### Things are hotting up

Some gases are called 'greenhouse' gases. This is because when they are in the atmosphere they act like a blanket that traps heat on Earth. Normally this is good because we want the Earth to be warm. But too much greenhouse gas in the atmosphere could cause the Earth to become uncomfortably warm.

### So the Earth's getting hotter – why do we need to worry?

Because even just a few degrees of warming can have a huge effect on the weather, the sea levels, wildlife, plant growth and more. We're seeing signs of this already, but if we keep burning fossil fuels at such a fast rate, our families could be living very different lives by 2050.

### Did you know?

The roofs of many London buses are now painted white, which reflects heat and reduces overheating.

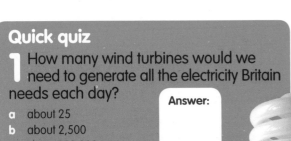

## Quick quiz

**1** How many wind turbines would we need to generate all the electricity Britain needs each day?

**Answer:**

a  about 25
b  about 2,500
c  about 250,000

**2** If each home in Britain used three energy-saving light bulbs, we'd save enough electricity to:

**Answer:**

a  operate all Britain's street lights
b  make 1,000 cups of tea
c  power all of Wales

Answers on page 47

## Danger – cow burping!

Some animals produce so much gas – in the form of big burps – that it spreads around Earth's atmosphere and contributes to global warming! Cows and other grazing animals are the biggest offenders as their burps contain methane – a very powerful greenhouse gas. And a single cow can burp up to 400 litres of gas per day! Multiply that by a billion and you can see that there could be a problem…

## Help! How do we stop cow burps?

Scientists are currently experimenting with cows' diets to see if certain foods will reduce the amount of burps produced in a day. They do this by attaching huge burp-collecting backpacks to the cow!

## Big ideas

Maybe what we need is a really ingenious planet-saving idea. Take a look at the four below – all are solutions which have been thought up by real scientists – apart from one! Which is it?

a  putting mirrors in space to reflect solar radiation
b  making artificial trees to 'suck' carbon dioxide out of the atmosphere
c  creating more clouds to reflect heat from the Sun by firing soot into the atmosphere
d  making a giant machine, similar to a vacuum cleaner, which will 'suck up' the greenhouse gases

**Answer:**

What colour are burps?
**Burple!**

29

# What Are Things Made Of?

**There are so many kinds of materials, all useful for different jobs.**

## Marvellous materials

There's wood, so versatile it can be used for making paper or building houses. There's wool, so warm that a sheep can stand in the snow all winter. Man-made materials such as plastic can be made both strong and flexible, great for making toys, phones and just about anything else you can think of.

## Reduce and reuse

Many materials can be reused to make new things – which could reduce our rubbish mountains. Before you throw anything away, think about whether you can use it again – perhaps turning it into something completely different!

This dress is made of stainless steel wire.

## The Cloak of Cans

Look for a stunning cloak, made from an incredible 2,500 square pieces of aluminium and steel. All the pieces were cut from drinking cans – nearly 300 of them! Aluminium drink cans can be recycled but can also be made into jewellery, coasters and even toys!

Why don't aliens recycle their rubbish? **Because they're already green!**

### Did you know?
On average, each person in the UK throws away **seven times** his or her body weight in rubbish each year!

Steel, glass, wood, felt, acrylic, fur, stone, rubber – there's an array of fascinating materials to touch and feel at the colourful Materials House in **Challenge of Materials** (first floor).

## Clever clothes

Over a million tonnes of old clothes end up in landfill every year. What will you do with yours?

a   throw them in the rubbish bin
b   take them to a clothes recycling bank
c   donate them to a charity shop
d   refashion them into something new

Answer:

**b**, **c** and **d** are all good options – but refashioning your clothes has got to be the most fun way to be green! Why not:

- Turn a pair of old jeans into shorts by simply cutting them off above the knee.

- Breathe life into an old T-shirt by sewing on felt shapes, beads or using fabric paints to design a groovy picture.

- Re-style an old T-shirt or top by chopping off the sleeves or changing the neckline.

## Where am I?

Can you find a spectacular glass bridge in **Challenge of Materials?** It will 'respond' to you in sound and light as you walk across it!

# Everyday Science

## Science is all around us, even in the most everyday objects…

Find me in
**Making the Modern World**

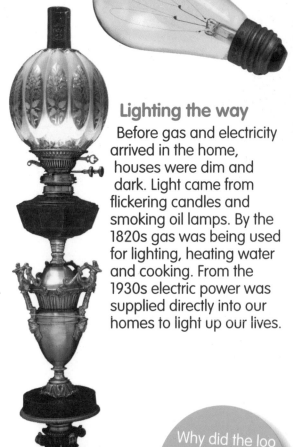

## Lighting the way

Before gas and electricity arrived in the home, houses were dim and dark. Light came from flickering candles and smoking oil lamps. By the 1820s gas was being used for lighting, heating water and cooking. From the 1930s electric power was supplied directly into our homes to light up our lives.

Why did the loo paper roll down the hill?
**To get to the bottom!**

## Toilet trouble

Before proper toilets a killer disease called cholera was always a threat – as raw sewage (that's wee and poo!) would often seep into people's drinking water. Eventually the government passed laws requiring houses to have some kind of flushing toilet. This 'washout closet' was patented by J. G. Jennings in 1852.

## Did you know?

The Romans used sponges, Henry VIII used a flannel and ordinary people used to use newspaper – or hay – to wipe their bottoms!

## Keeping time

Wouldn't life be strange if we didn't know what time it was? We take clocks and watches for granted but there was a time when they didn't exist. People measured time using water, sun and sand.

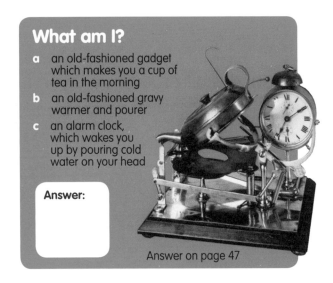

## What am I?

a an old-fashioned gadget which makes you a cup of tea in the morning

b an old-fashioned gravy warmer and pourer

c an alarm clock, which wakes you up by pouring cold water on your head

Answer:

Answer on page 47

## Clever clockwork

Once clockwork was invented, people could tell the time pretty accurately. Then, in 1656, Christiaan Huygens designed the world's first pendulum clock. It was far more reliable than any other mechanical timepiece. For nearly 300 years, the best clocks in the world used pendulums.

Why was the clock sad?
**Because it had no-one to tock to!**

Want to know how toilets really work? Visit **The Secret Life of the Home** (basement) – give the see-through toilet a flush and see what happens inside.

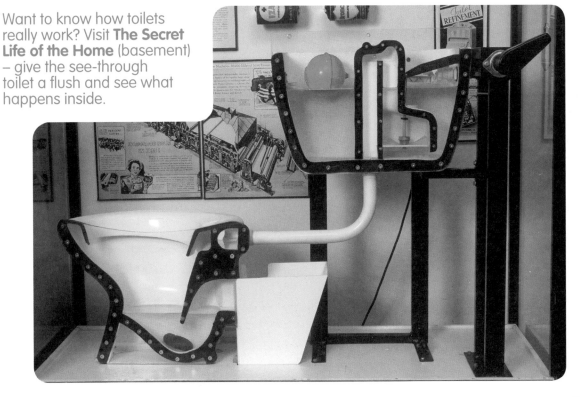

# Techno Talk

## With email, text and phone, communicating has never been easier. But it wasn't always like this…

### Radio days

Long before emails came along, people used the electric telegraph to 'wire' messages to faraway places. By the 1890s radio communication had been developed. James Clerk Maxwell first suggested that radio waves behave as light does. Later, Guglielmo Marconi came up with a communications system that everyone could use – the radio!

How did the computer get out of jail?
**He used the Escape key!**

### Babbage's Difference Engine

**Brilliant inventor Charles Babbage drew designs for this enormous automatic calculator over 150 years ago. He called it a 'Difference Engine'. In 1834, he came up with another idea – the Analytical Engine. This design contained many of the ideas behind the modern computer – incredible for its time.**

### Did you know?

The Science Museum finished building Difference Engine No. 2 to Babbage's original design – and proved that it would have worked if he had been able to finish it.

Find me in **Computing**

## Turn on your TV

At one time, families would gather round to hear the news and enjoy shows on the radio. But by 1936 television was a reality. Queen Elizabeth II's Coronation in June 1953 encouraged many people to buy a TV set for the first time – it would have looked something like this Bush TV. By 1969 millions of people watched as the first man set foot on the Moon. TV was here to stay.

**Did you know?**
In 1936 a TV cost about the same as a small car!

## The Computer Age begins

It's hard to imagine a world without computers or the Internet, but in the 1970s there were hardly any home computer users. The Apple I was created in a garage by three enthusiasts and was just a basic circuit board to which display units and keyboards could be added.

## Will computers ever be cleverer than people?

It's difficult to say – many computers today can already 'think' faster and better than people, but only in very limited ways. For now, at least, computers are not very intelligent or clever by our standards. But in the future – who knows?

## The King of Pings

In the 1970s 'Pong' was the first ever home video game. No characters, levels, colour or sound effects… but kids at the time still thought it was the greatest! Why not try a game in **The Secret Life of the Home**? (basement)

For more up-to-date fun, try Launchball, the addictive online game that brings **Launchpad** into your home. See the Science Museum website at **www.sciencemuseum.org.uk** for more details.

# Super Scientists

**The Science Museum celebrates many remarkable people from all fields of science – here are just a few.**

Why did the scientist put a knocker on her door?
**She wanted to win the No-bell prize!**

### Marie Curie 1867–1934

A physicist and chemist from Poland, she pioneered the discovery and understanding of radioactivity and how it could be used in treating cancer. She was also the first person ever to receive two Nobel Prizes!

**Did you know?**
Marie's original notebook is so radioactive that no-one can look at it!

### Brilliant Brunel

One of Britain's greatest engineers, Isambard Kingdom Brunel, designed the Great Eastern steamship (see page 19). Brunel wasn't just good at ships. He also designed tunnels, railway lines and bridges.

### Amazing Amy

In 1930 Amy Johnson flew from London all the way to Australia in her famous Gipsy Moth Jason I – a 2-seat single-engine wooden biplane. Amy became the first ever woman to make this nerve-racking solo flight.

### Isaac Newton 1643–1727

He named the colours of the rainbow; he is said to have invented the cat flap; he thought about how apples fall from trees! He is possibly one of the most important and influential people in human history. Sir Isaac Newton revolutionised our outlook on life through his amazing explanation of gravity and the wonders of his three laws of motion.

## Ada Lovelace 1815–1852

She is often described as the world's first computer programmer – even though computers hadn't actually been invented in Victorian times! Ada worked with Charles Babbage and made important observations about his Analytical Engine. She truly understood the potential of this machine to do so much more than just calculating numbers.

## Edwin Hubble 1889–1953

Edwin Hubble completely changed our understanding of the universe when he became the first person to show that the universe is expanding. This and other achievements make him one of the most important astronomers of the 20th century. The famous Hubble Space Telescope is named after him.

## Al-Jazari 1136–1206

This brilliant Islamic thinker wrote a book in which he described 50 ingenious mechanical devices – everything from pumps to clocks to camshafts and crankshafts (which later became central parts of the steam engine and internal combustion engine). One of his most famous inventions was a clock shaped like an elephant, which was entirely powered by water.

## Quick quiz

The Nobel Prize – named for Alfred Nobel, the creator of the prize – is awarded to those who make outstanding achievements in physics, chemistry, medicine, literature and peace. But which invention was Alfred Nobel responsible for?

a dynamite
b the DVD player
c the doorbell

**Answer:**

Answer on page 47

## Alan Turing 1912–1954

A brilliant mathematician and wartime code-breaker. During World War II, Turing came up with a method that could 'decrypt' German coded messages – which ensured that the Allies remained one step ahead of the game. An expert in computer science and artificial intelligence, Alan Turing played a hugely important role in the development of the modern computer.

# Super Science at Home

**Launchpad** is the most popular and buzzing area of the Museum – and no wonder! With so many gadgets to test and fascinating things to investigate, it's quite possibly the most fun you can have while learning about science. Now you can bring the excitement of **Launchpad** into your home by trying these great experiments.

## EAR GONGS!

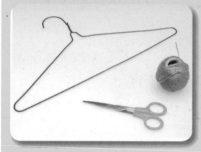

2 Wrap the other end(s) of the string(s) around your finger(s), like this...

3 Put your finger(s) in your ears! (Not too far, though.)

4 Lean forward so your object hangs down, then knock it against the table.

**BONNGG!**

### You will need:
- 1 coat hanger or other metal object, e.g. cutlery
- 1 metre of string or thread
- A hard surface to bang it against, e.g. a desk

### What to do:
1 Choose a metal object and tie on one or two pieces of string like this...

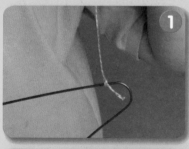

### Stuff to think about:
- What does it sound like before you put the string in your ears compared with after? Why?
- Where is the sound coming from? How can we hear it?
- Why do we need the string? What would happen if you tried to put the hanger directly against your ear? (Don't try with any sharp bits!)

### Things to try:
- Try different types of string or thread.
- Try with different objects made of metal and other materials.
- What happens if a friend ties a piece of string on to the object? Does the sound get louder, softer or stay the same? Can you both hear it?
- What if your friend ties a thread on to one of your strings? Will he/she be able to hear the sound too? Can you still hear it? How has the vibration travelled?

### Sounds interesting?
Head over to Sound Bite in **Launchpad**, where you 'bite' on a metal rod to find out how sound vibrations travel through hard materials – like your teeth!

## Bubbles, bubbles everywhere

Watch as bubbles get thinner, change colour, stretch and finally – ping! – disappear at the fabulous Bubble Wall. Then have a home-made bubble bonanza…

### BUBBLE TROUBLE!

**You will need:**

- String
- Drinking straws
- Scissors
- Bubble mixture poured into a plate

**First method:**

1   Cut a piece of straw about 5 cm long.
2   Push the string through the straw (you can try different lengths of string).

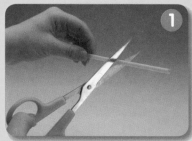

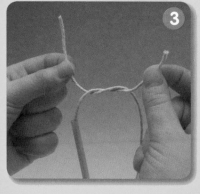

3   Tie both ends of the string together.
4   Holding on to the straw, dip the string into your bubble mix, take a deep breath and blow.

**Second method:**

1   Push one straw into the end of another straw.
2   Bend the straws round and connect the other ends in the

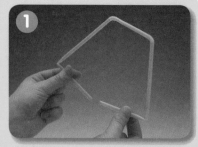

same way, to make a loop. Dip the loop in your bubble mix and, holding it carefully, blow through it to make a bubble.

## No glues or screws!

In **Launchpad**, try constructing an arched bridge so strong that it could (so they say) support a polar bear! But dare you step on to it yourself?! Then at home, see who can build the tallest tower possible – from spaghetti!

## SPAGHETTI CHALLENGE!

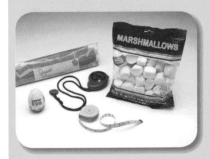

2  Using only marshmallows (you can break them up) to stick the spaghetti together, start building a tower.

3  When the time's up, place the egg on top and see if your tower will hold it up for 30 seconds.

4  Did it work? How high did you get? Do you think you could do better? Why not have a competition with your friends?

Find out the secrets of constructing bridges and superstructures in the fabulous **Stronger By Design** show!

### You will need:

- A large handful of spaghetti
- 6 marshmallows
- 1 chocolate egg
- A tape measure
- A watch

### What to do:

1  Set a time limit: five or ten minutes, say.

## Liquid limits

In **Launchpad**, try pushing air bubbles through different kinds of liquids and see how they move in Sticky Liquids. Then see what happens at home when you try to combine two very different liquids.

# LAVA LUNACY!

### You will need:

- 1 litre plastic bottle
- Funnel
- Vegetable oil
- Water
- Food colouring
- Effervescent tablets, e.g. vitamin or indigestion tablets

### What to do:

1. Fill a clean bottle 1/3 with water.
2. Add a few drops of food colouring.
3. Fill the rest of the bottle with vegetable oil.
4. Break up a tablet and add it to the bottle, about half a tablet at a time.
5. Watch the lava blobs!

### What's happening?

Water and oil do not mix, as you probably know! This is because water is denser than oil, and therefore sinks to the bottom. The food colouring mixes only with the water, which is why the oil stays its normal colour. The tablet falls through the oil and when it reacts with the water, it creates tiny bubbles of carbon dioxide, or $CO_2$. This gas floats to the surface, carrying drops of coloured water with it. When the bubbles pop and the gas is released, the denser water sinks back down.

### Things to try:

- Don't use yellow food colouring; it doesn't show up against the oil!
- Try using salt instead of an effervescent tablet; add about 2 teaspoons at a time.
- You can also try adding things like glitter to the mix if you want your lamp to look even prettier!

There are several different live **Launchpad** shows – all of them brilliant fun to watch. Check with the **Launchpad** desk for times.

What do you get if a cow jumps up and down?
**Milk shakes!**

# MILK MAGIC

## You will need:

- 1 pint of whole milk
- Flat plate
- 4 different colours of food colouring
- Washing-up liquid
- Cotton buds
- Pipette

2 Using the pipette, add one drop of each food colouring near the middle of the milk.

3 Dip a cotton bud in the washing-up liquid.

4 Place the bud in the centre of the milk.

5 Watch the colours swirl!

## What's happening?

Milk is made of water, vitamins, minerals, proteins and fats.

When the washing-up liquid is added, it makes the fats and proteins in the milk spread out. (This is why we use soap for washing up.) This happens very quickly, causing the liquid to swirl.

The food-colouring molecules bump together, letting us see the usually invisible activity.

## Top tips

- Don't stir the milk, just touch it with the tip of the cotton bud.
- Try placing cotton buds at different places in the milk.
- Repeat the demonstration using water instead of milk. Will you get the same reaction of colour?

## What to do:

1 Pour enough milk in the plate to cover the bottom.

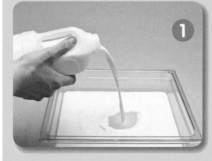

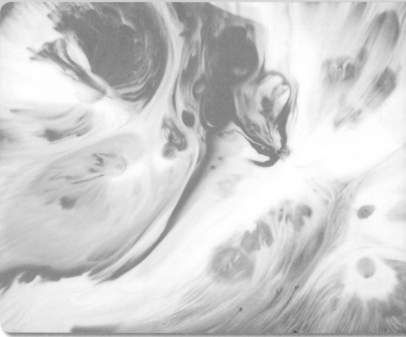

# GRAVITY-DEFYING WATER

## You will need:
- A jug of water
- A glass
- Some thick card
- A dish or sink

## What to do:
1. Fill the glass with water.
2. Place the card on the top of the glass and rub it to press the card against the rim of the glass.
3. Turn the glass over while holding on to the card. Do this over the dish or sink.
4. When the glass is upside down let go of the card and the water and card should stay in place.

## What's happening?
In order for the water to fall out of the glass, air has to replace it. This cannot happen, as the water on the rim of the glass has formed a seal with the card. As well as this the air pressure in the room is pushing up on the card.

Although the water seal is relatively sticky, it will not last forever. In time gravity will break the seal by pulling the card and the water down.

## Top tips
- Always keep the card flat.
- A piece of laminated card will also work.

# BLOW-UP BALLOON

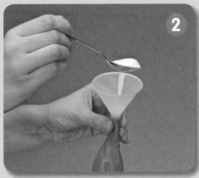

## You will need:
- 1 small plastic bottle
- Vinegar
- Baking soda or bicarbonate of soda
- 1 balloon
- Teaspoon
- Funnel

## What to do:
1. Put 1 cm of water into the bottle, and then add about 2 cm of vinegar.
2. Then use the funnel to put 2 teaspoons of baking soda into the balloon.
3. Carefully place the balloon over the mouth of the bottle, making sure none of the baking powder falls into the bottle.
4. Then lift the end of the balloon and pour all the baking powder into the bottle in one go.
5. Shake it well and then watch the balloon inflate all by itself!

## Top tip
- The more vinegar and baking soda you use, the more extreme the reaction!

## What's happening?
This is a reaction between a base (baking soda) and an acid (vinegar). This reaction produces a by-product, a gas called carbon dioxide or $CO_2$, one of the gases we breathe out. The gas produced by the reaction cannot escape and therefore fills the balloon.

# The Science Museum and Me

There are more than 15,000 items in the Museum

The Science Museum has been around for more than 100 years – since Queen Victoria's time!

Roughly 2.8 million people visited the Museum in 2009

**I came to the Science Museum on**

. . . . . . . . . . . . . . . . . . . . . . . . . . . . . .

**My favourite parts of the Museum are**

. . . . . . . . . . . . . . . . . . . . . . . . . . . . . . . . . . . . . . . . . .

. . . . . . . . . . . . . . . . . . . . . . . . . . . . . . . . . . . . . . . . . .

. . . . . . . . . . . . . . . . . . . . . . . . . . . . . . . . . . . . . . . . . .

**My favourite objects in the Museum are**

. . . . . . . . . . . . . . . . . . . . . . . . . . . . . . . . . . . . . . . . . .

. . . . . . . . . . . . . . . . . . . . . . . . . . . . . . . . . . . . . . . . . .

. . . . . . . . . . . . . . . . . . . . . . . . . . . . . . . . . . . . . . . . . .

. . . . . . . . . . . . . . . . . . . . . . . . . . . . . .

. . . . . . . . . . . . . . . . . . . . . . . . . . . . . .

The Museum has seven floors and is over 500 metres long

44

Can you think of a great new invention or idea?
Draw your own Super Science design here!

# Answers

## Pages 2 and 3: Weird and Wonderful
**The locations are:**
Find the Banshee aircraft in **Flight** (third floor).
Find the original Orrery in **Science in the 18th Century** (third floor).
Find Bleadon Man in **Who am I?** (first floor, Wellcome Wing).
Find the carpet dress in **Challenge of Materials** (first floor).
Find the bubble car in **Making the Modern World** (ground floor).
Find the Klein bottle in **Mathematics** (second floor).
Find the one-million-volt particle accelerator in **Making the Modern World** (ground floor).
Find the 'baked bean' telescope in **Cosmos & Culture** (first floor).

## Page 6: Exploring Space
**Quick quiz** The answer is **a**. The first living creature to be launched into space was a dog called Laika, who was sent into space on board the Soviet spacecraft Sputnik II on 3 November 1957. Unfortunately, Laika did not survive the journey. A statue of a dog on top of a rocket now stands in her honour near Moscow.

## Page 9: Life in Space
**What am I?** The answer is **c** – a heat-resistant tile that protects the outside of the Space Shuttle. Hundred of tiles of different sizes and types cover the Shuttle. Some have a black ceramic coating, like the one shown. They protect parts of the Shuttle from the incredibly high temperatures caused by the friction of re-entering the atmosphere – somewhere between 1,200 and 2,300 degrees Fahrenheit! That's unbelievably hot – but you'll be relieved to hear that the Shuttle's thermal protection system is very effective and has flown more than a hundred astronaut crews safely.

## Page 10: Space Investigation
**Quick quiz** The answer is **c**. It takes the Hubble telescope about 97 minutes to complete one orbit of the Earth. (Source: Hubble website)

## Page 13: Steaming Ahead
**What am I?** The answer is **a** – a power loom for weaving cloth. Power looms were driven by steam engines and their invention helped transform the textile industry during the Industrial Revolution. In 1825, a weaver using a normal hand loom could weave about 100 yards of cloth a week. However, a power loom could weave 250 yards. By 1850 there were thousands of power looms in operation in Britain's mills and factories.

## Page 15: Flying Machines
**Quick quiz** The answer is **b** – Orville and Wilbur.

## Page 16: On the Road
**Quick quiz** The answer is **b**. The top speed of a Bugatti Veyron EB 16.4 – one of the most expensive cars in the world – is 253 mph (408 km/h).

## Page 18: Ship Ahoy!
**Quick quiz** Starboard is right and port is left. A good way of remembering this is that there are four letters in the words 'port' and 'left'.

## Page 21: Marvellous Medicine
**What am I?** The answer is **b**. This is an experimental MRI brain scanner 'helmet' for children. It was used at the Hammersmith Hospital as a possible way of getting the best picture of a child's brain. The helmet

is nicknamed 'Jedi' because it looks a bit like those worn by Jedi knights in the 'Star Wars' films. The coils on the helmet are 'aerials' for picking up MRI signals.

## Page 23: Your Amazing Brain

**Quick quiz** The answer is **a**. A sperm whale has the heaviest brain, weighing in at an average 7.8 kg, closely followed by an elephant, with an average 7.5 kg. A human's brain weighs in at an average 1.5 kg.

## Page 24: What Makes You, You?

**What am I?** The answer is **a**. Hand-held testing devices like these are currently being developed to analyse DNA in a quick turnaround time. They could have lots of uses in the future, e.g. doctors could use them to test patients for diseases and investigators could use them to analyse DNA evidence at crime scenes.

## Page 27: Exciting Energy

**Quick quiz** The answer is **b**. The World Energy Council thinks that we can supply oil at the current rate for 30 more years. But some people disagree with this – they say that there are plenty more fossil fuels left that we haven't yet discovered.

## Page 29: Future Earth

**Quick quiz 1)** The answer is **c** – it would take about 250,000 wind turbines to power Britain entirely from wind, but they'd only make enough electricity on a windy day. Today we have only a tiny fraction of this number. By

using more wind power in the future, Britain is aiming to make big cuts in the amount of greenhouse gases that we pump into the air.

**2)** The answer is **a** – three energy-saving light bulbs in each house would save enough electricity to power all of Britain's street lights. All of us can help by doing simple things to save energy around the house.

## Page 29: Future Earth

**Big ideas** All the ideas are real ones that have been thought up by scientists to help counter global warming – apart from **d**. There is no vacuum cleaner that we know of that will suck up greenhouse gases!

## Page 33: Everyday Science

**What am I?** The answer is **a**. This is a machine that makes tea automatically, normally placed on a bedside table so that you can be woken up with a hot cup of tea. This Victorian 'teasmade' used a clockwork alarm clock, a gas ring and pilot light to heat the water and make the tea.

## Page 37: Super Scientists

**Quick quiz** The answer is **a**. Alfred Nobel was a Swedish chemist and inventor who, in 1866, came up with a form of nitroglycerine that he believed could safely be used as an explosive. Called dynamite, it was patented the year after. Nobel later used his fortune to set up the Nobel Prize.

© Science Museum 2010
ISBN: 978-0-330-52340-0

**Thanks to:**
Mark Bezodis, Tilly Blyth, Alison Boyle, Jennifer Burgos, Holly Cave, Raphael Chanay, Karen Davies, Selina Hurley, Doug Millard, Susan Mossman, Andrew Nahum, Jonathan Newby, Helen Peavitt, David Rooney, Ben Russell, Sam Spicer, Stuart Umbo, Nicola Upton-Swift, Jane Wess, Jammie Williams

**Project Manager for Science Museum:** Deborah Bloxam
**Project Manager for Macmillan Children's Books:** Gaby Morgan
**Author and Project Editor:** Amanda Li
**Designer:** Dan Newman
**Illustrator:** Mike Phillips

**Printed in Italy**

**Picture credits:**
Science & Society Picture Library
Science Museum Photo Studio
iStockphoto.com: angry girl p22 (LugoStock), chimpanzee p23 (GlobalP), boy with burger p25 (Photo Euphoria), wind turbine p29 (fotoVoyager), old jeans p31 (Jitalia17), sponge p32 (bkindler)

**Sponsors:**
The Science Museum is grateful for the support of public-sector organisations, companies, trusts and foundations, members, volunteers, Patrons and individuals, which allows us to open new exhibitions, run innovative visitor programmes and take events out to schools and communities.

**Gallery funders**
**Antenna** – Established with the founding support of SITA Trust and The Royal Commission for the Exhibition of 1851, with additional support from EADS, The Royal Academy of Engineering, the journal *Science* and AAAS, and *Nature*.

**atmosphere …exploring climate science** – Principal Sponsors: Shell and Siemens. Major Sponsor: Bank of America Merrill Lynch. Major Funder: The Garfield Weston Foundation. With additional support from: the Department for Environment, Food and Rural Affairs, the Founders Circle of the climate science gallery and the Patrons of the Science Museum.

**Making the Modern World** – Heritage Lottery Fund.

**The Science and Art of Medicine/Glimpses of Medical History** – Wellcome Trust.

**Who am I?** – Principal Funder: Wellcome Trust. Major Sponsors: GlaxoSmithKline and Life Technologies Foundation.

**Major Programme funders**
**Talk Science** – BP.